THE JAILER WHO CHANGED HIS MIND

ACTS 16:19-34 FOR CHILDREN

Written by Carol Granger

Illustrated by Jim Roberts

Concordia Publishing House

ARCH Books

CONCORDIA PUBLISHING HOUSE LTD.
117/123 GOLDEN LANE, LONDON, E. C. 1.
PRINTED IN ENGLAND
ISBN 0-570-06058-3

Theo was a jailer
whose job had always been
to guard the jail in town,
to lock the prisoners in.

"My job is quite important,"
bold Theo now would say.
"With bad men locked up tight,
we're safe both night and day."

Then one day news reached Theo's jail
of trouble in the square.
"I hear two men have been accused;
a mob is gathering there."

He left another man in charge
and hurried with the crowd
to where he heard the sound of voices
rising, shouting, growing loud.

"Have you heard of Paul and Silas?"
asked a friend along the way.
"They've been stirring up the people,
telling folks to disobey.

"They have changed poor Jasper's slave girl,
who told fortunes for a fee.
They've destroyed her special powers;
Jasper's mad as he can be."

Theo felt his heart beat faster.
Now he clenched his fists in rage.
"How dare these men teach evil ways!
How dare they steal poor Jasper's wage!"

"Punish them! Punish them!" everyone shouted.
Voices and curses were splitting the air.
"Strip off their clothing,
and whip them both soundly.
Grab them and do it right here in the square."

The leaders then brought
Paul and Silas to Theo.
"Tie them and chain them
and put them away."

He cursed them and pushed them
far back in a dungeon.
He slammed the door, locked it,
and said, "Here you stay."

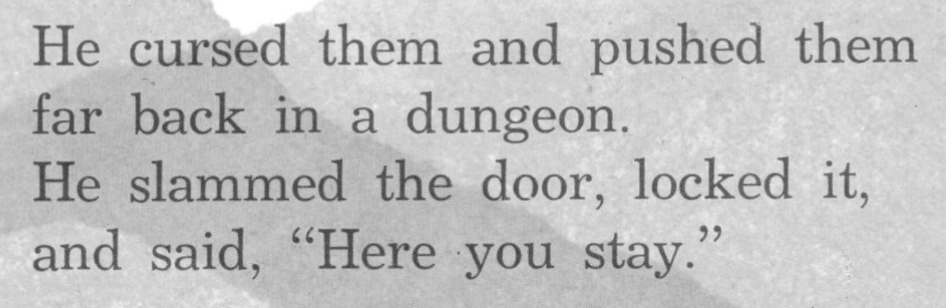

At midnight Theo heard some noises
coming from the prisoners' cell.
"Could it be that I hear singing?
I'd better see if all is well."

Theo went to check the prisoners.
There was music in the air!
From the darkest cell of prison
Paul and Silas sang with prayer.

As he walked, the jailer felt
the ground beneath him start to quake.
He dropped the flaming torch he held
as the walls began to shake.

Then he saw the doors all open.
"My prisoners must have got away,"
he thought, and fearing all was lost,
he drew his sword, himself to slay.

Then from the dark a clear voice called,
"We're here, my friend. You need not fear.
Put back your sword. Don't kill yourself.
All your prisoners still are here!"

Trembling, Theo called for lights and held them up to see.

Why, sure enough, the prisoners all
were safe as safe could be!

"O sirs," he said to Paul and Silas,
"I've made a big mistake.
I've beaten and imprisoned you,
and still you do not hate.

"Just now your doors were opened,
yet you did not run away.
Can you tell me, sirs, the reason
why you've acted in this way?"

Paul and Silas gladly told him
of the Saviour, Jesus Christ.
When he'd listened to their story,
Theo asked to be baptized.

"Will you come and tell my family?
I am thankful if you do.
You have changed my life through Jesus.
I want them to know Him too."

Theo freed his happy prisoners,
washed their sores and gave them food.
Baptized then with all his family,
Theo said, "The Lord is good."

Happiness and laughter filled
the jailer's house that night.
And the family celebration
lasted till the morning light.

DEAR PARENTS:

The author of this book uses her imagination to describe the jailer at Philippi as a man who was glad to lock Paul and Silas in his prison. He was not a follower of Jesus Christ and was not in sympathy with the words and actions of Paul and Silas.

But he changed his mind, for the power of the Holy Spirit influenced him through the witness of Paul and Silas. Confident of Christ, these two men sang praises in the middle of the night. They were expressing what Paul said in his letter to the Philippians: "I have learned, in whatever state I am, to be content." (Phil. 4:11)

Their beating and their imprisonment were not causes for doubt, complaint, or despair but brought new opportunities to preach the saving Gospel of Christ Crucified.

Talk with your child about what God did through Paul and Silas. Encourage him to see that God can bring good out of disappointment and trouble. God gave Paul and Silas courage and confidence even when they were beaten and imprisoned. He changed the terrified jailer's mind when he heard the Gospel of Christ from Paul and Silas. God still changes the minds of people when Christians tell of their faith.

THE EDITOR